TO Emma-Jane.
6th Birthday
from Fraser & Nicky
x x x x

Illustrations by Gerda Muller
Text by Rosalind Sutton

A Cat
Called Friday

BRIMAX   BOOKS   CAMBRIDGE   ENGLAND

Nicky was happy and excited. His mother had promised him a kitten. Off they went, carrying the basket. Nicky would choose the kitten himself, to be his very own. He would love it, and take care of it. It would be his special friend always.

6

They knocked on Mrs. Brown's door . . . . "Please, have you a kitten for me?" asked Nicky. "Come in, Nicky. Come and see all my cats."

8

Nicky was amazed! He had never seen so many! "Thirteen altogether," Mrs. Brown said. 'There must be hundreds' . . . thought Nicky . . . ginger, tabby, white, black, grey, tortoise-shell and Siamese! They were everywhere . . . except on the ceiling!

Then he saw the mother cat with three tiny babies. Nicky loved the dark grey one and wanted it at once . . . "I'm afraid not, Nicky. They are much too young," explained Mrs. Brown. Mother cat kept watch.

Would this little boy touch her kittens? Out she stepped, holding the grey one in her mouth. "Oh, she's hurting it!" cried Nicky. "Don't worry," said Mrs. Brown. "She'll carry them very gently to a safer place — a cupboard, perhaps. She's afraid you'll take one. They're only a week old. Three more days before their eyes open. She feeds them. They need her for another six weeks."

"Would you save one for me?" Nicky asked. "Of course, if you can wait that long," said Mrs. Brown. "I'll wait," he answered. "Very well. Come each Friday, to see how he's getting on." Nicky counted the days! The kitten grew quickly. Soon, it trotted towards him to pull his laces! Nicky was delighted!

12

He played with the kitten and talked to it. "This is your basket to go home in," he whispered. "Do you like it?" He let it climb in and out to get used to the basket. The kitten purred when Nicky cuddled it, licked his fingers and gave him tiny bites. Sometimes it would purr itself off to sleep, then wake refreshed for another game. The cord of Nicky's jacket was a grand play-thing. Holding it with claws and teeth the kitten would wait for Nicky to pull it gently away.

Everything was ready. Nicky had bought dishes. His mother had lined the basket. They filled a deep tray with saw-dust for its lavatory. Cats are easily trained and very clean. At last the day came. "It's Friday, Mummy!" Nicky shouted. "How about its name?" she asked. "It's Friday!" he kept on saying. "It's Friday!" So, they called the kitten 'Friday'.

CAT LITTER

14

He liked his new home. He
tried his basket and his tray!
He hid under the furniture,
turned somersaults and dived
into the paper-basket! This
kitten Friday: he delighted the
whole family!

15

Just look at him! Didn't he want milk that day? Sometimes he'd 'mew' for more. Once he put his paw in the handle of the dish, tipping it! . . . He loved the puddle! A wash was needed after that bit of fun! He used his long rough tongue.

The ball teased him; it was always rolling away. He caught it and held on, spreading his claws: five on each front paw, four on the back. Look at them! Sharp for hunting. But cats can retract them — draw them in; then the paws are soft as velvet. Friday had sensitive whiskers, to feel his way in the dark; although cats have good night-vision. See in the picture, the black pupil opens wider, letting in every ray of light. So, he can see better. Nicky liked to watch Friday's day-time eyes change to his night-time ones.

F—B°

What games they had together! One favourite was chasing the piece of paper. Nicky dangled it on a string. Friday jumped, danced and rolled. He'd growl and tear bits off. Everything he did was pretty to watch.

18

Sometimes, he'd walk away, pretending he was tired. Then, out he'd dart, from behind a chair. That made Nicky jump!

19

One day, Friday was squatting in the corner. He needed his saw-dust tray. Nicky's mother carried him there, quickly! She held him correctly, by the scruff of his neck. How thankful he was!

Cats need to sharpen their claws, just as we need to cut our nails. The trouble is, they choose the best chairs! Daddy fixed an old mat round a piece of tree trunk . . . an indoor sharpening-post! Friday loved it!

CF—B'

He was praised when he used
his post. They laughed when
he scratched and bit his toys.
But if he clawed the curtains
and covers! Oh, my goodness!
He was in trouble! Why did
they make all this fuss about
furniture? It was difficult to
understand.

22

Another thing puzzled him. Why did Nicky go off to school? Mummy cuddled him then, and he slept in his basket. But when Nicky returned calling, "Friday! Friday!" he'd prick up his ears, and be ready for a game. Nicky was always gentle. He'd never hurt Friday.

23

Where Nicky lived, they had a balcony. It was pretty with geraniums and hanging ivy. Nicky's mother grew a pot of green grass for Friday. You see, cats chew grass to make themselves sick, to spew up the fur they swallow when washing.

24

Friday liked the balcony. He enjoyed climbing up the wire netting. One day he leaned over too far and slipped off the top rail. Nicky saw him!

26

He flew down to his rescue. "My Friday!" he kept saying. "My poor Friday!" People stopped in the street. "Under the car!" yelled the road sweeper. Nicky went under the car too. "Friday! ... Friday! ... Where are you?" ... "Meeeew!" There! On the wheel! So frightened! Holding Friday close, Nicky wriggled out. He whispered gently, loving him, till Friday was fast asleep.

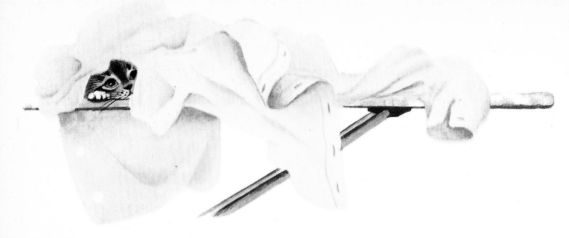

There is a saying, 'Cats always fall on their feet!' Friday must have done — he hadn't hurt himself. He awoke full of life and mischief. He liked the warm ironing board. How cosy to crawl into a cave of soft, clean shirt! And fresh minced beef? Excellent, of course! ... How about a bit of knitting? ... He knitted himself up with that! All the same, — everybody loved Friday!

29

The summer holidays came. They were going to Granny's. She lived on a farm. "How about Friday, Mummy?" "We'll take him," she said. "He couldn't be left alone." So, everything was fine. Nicky started to pack.

Friday enjoyed the drive and the view. When he began to wander about, Nicky popped him in the basket and fastened the lid. Couldn't have him distracting the driver. They arrived safely. There was Granny, coming to meet them!

What delights for Friday! He was out exploring the first day.
He loved the tall grasses to hide in and to prance over. All the
different smells of the earth, insects and farm animals!
Everything excited him. He was a hunter, out in the woods for
the first time!

32

That grasshopper now, he'd catch him! . . . And how about
these funny little quacking things? . . . Oh, my! You will be in
such trouble, Friday! . . . What a good job Nicky arrived! He
was just in time to save the ducklings — and you, from
disaster!

F—C

Friday strolled into the cowshed. Jenny was milking and a
little puddle of milk had been spilt . . . Hmm. Delicious!
Swish! Swish, went the cow's tail! Friday liked it. Jenny
watched. If Friday pulled its tail, the cow might kick!

34

Jenny couldn't risk that. So: "Out Friday! Off you go!" she said. He went, licking his creamy mouth. A great hairy creature, with lolling tongue, stood in his way — Bruno, the sheep-dog. Friday bristled and spat! But Bruno guarded animals, he never hurt them. He made the kitten understand. Soon, they were friends, and Friday lay sleeping between his legs.

Another day Friday jumped onto the drinking trough. The water sparkled. He patted it ... mmm ... wet — like rain. It tasted quite good. He'd have a drink. Splash! He was in the water! Mee-ow! He struggled, he pushed his legs. Down ... up! Down ... up! He was swimming!

Poor Friday couldn't get out. He swam round and round crying, "Meeew . . . meeew!" At last Nicky heard and saved him. Back at the farm, they dried him and wrapped him in a big towel. Friday sat before the big kitchen fire, warm and happy. He worked hard, licking his fur smooth again.

That night, Friday awoke to howlings and calls from another cat. It was Tom, the farm rat-catcher. "Come on, young whipper-snapper! I'll teach you to poach on my territory! Mee-ow . . . wow-wow!" Friday had to go!

38

The fierce black cat waited and screamed. Friday joined in.
Louder and louder! "Take that, old cross-patch!" He landed
a blow on Tom's nose. But he hadn't a chance. Bleeding and
trembling he raced indoors!

The holiday was over. Granny was saying goodbye. Bruno
came to see them off. Where was Friday? Nicky was worried.
Did he like the farm so much he had hidden away? Nicky
would be very sad without him.

"Friday!" he called, "Friday, Friday!" Bruno gave a little
'Whoof!' Up marched his friend all ready to go home and
jumped in the car. "Come again, soon!" called Granny.
"Woof, woof!" added Bruno. "Bring Friday!"

FOR THOSE WHO WOULD LIKE TO KNOW MORE

The Cat family is highly developed. All cats are intelligent, swift and graceful, with keen sight and hearing. These wild animals are cats:— Lion and leopard (Africa and India): tiger (India and the Far East): cheetah (Africa, Arabia and India). The cheetah is the swiftest of all, and he purrs! There are also jaguars, pumas (Central and South America) and many lynxes. Sub-species of wild-cat live in Europe and Asia, except the tropics.

DOMESTIC CAT GONE WILD

TRUE WILD-CAT

A pure strain is still found in the British Isles. Larger, stronger, with broader tail than the domestic cat, it is yellowish-grey with dark bands and spots. It lives in remote highlands. Sometimes a domestic cat goes back to the wild, but it is not pure strain.

All cats are hunters. They have the claws for catching and the teeth for eating flesh. A well-fed domestic cat will catch birds, mice and insects. A cat is strong enough to kill a young rabbit if it gets the chance.

A cat has better night-vision than man. The pupil of his eye opens very wide to let in every ray of light. He is able to catch a mouse in dim light, or moonlight,

42

but he cannot see if it is dark. A cat does not see colours; everything is grey to him.

When you choose a kitten, don't take it from the mother too young. Six weeks old at the very least; two months is better. Your kitten should have bright eyes, upright clean ears and a firm, not bulging stomach. See that he has plenty of sleep. Leave clean water for him — he gets thirsty. Never give him raw fish or raw offal. Brush him gently. Play with him; a healthy kitten is full of fun. When you pick him up, don't squeeze him in the middle. Put one hand under the back legs to take the weight. Love him but don't pester him: cats like to be left alone sometimes.

Our cats probably came from Egypt. They had been domesticated there for 2,000 years B.C. and were regarded as sacred. Some eastern countries used them to guard their temples. Now, cats are our friends and are very useful. Nearly all ships have a cat to keep rats and mice away.

Some cats, Siamese or Manx, will wear a lead and collar and follow you, but others refuse. Cats are individual, they won't be forced. Their life-span is about twelve to fifteen years.

There are many different breeds of cats; here are some of them:

EUROPEAN

STRIPED TABBY   SPOTTED TABBY   GINGER and WHITE

SIAMESE

CHOCOLATE-POINT   BLUE-POINT